My name is Pryor.

I was born at home and so was my little brother, Pryce.

This is the story of Pryce being born.

Pryce grows in my Mommy's belly for a long time.

She is pregnant with my brother.

I like to kiss Mommy's belly.

My pregnant Mommy goes to a midwife.

Her name is Maria.

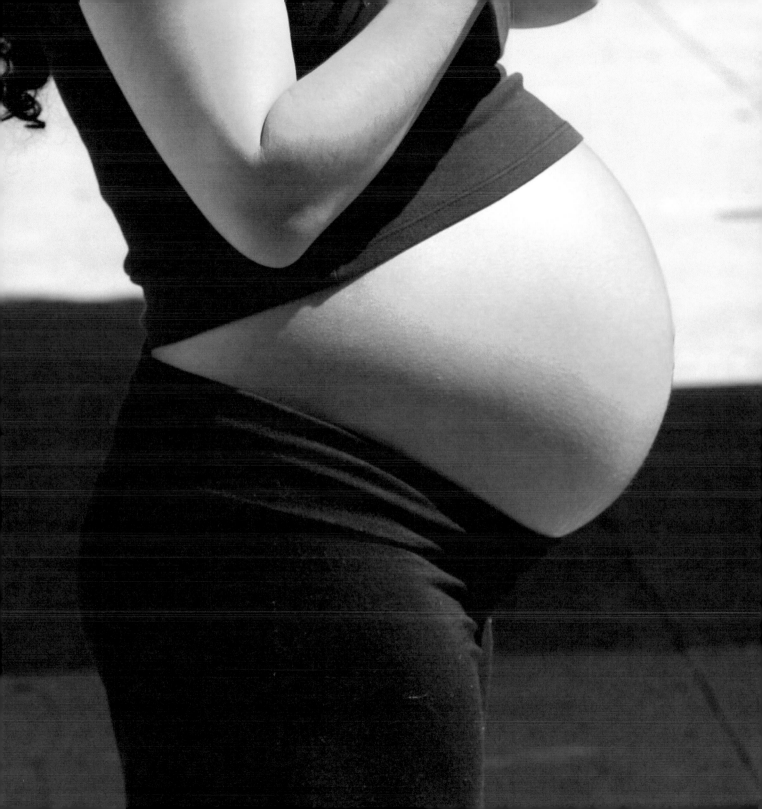

A midwife takes care of a mommy when she is pregnant and giving birth.

Maria the Midwife checks how a baby is growing inside the mommy's tummy.

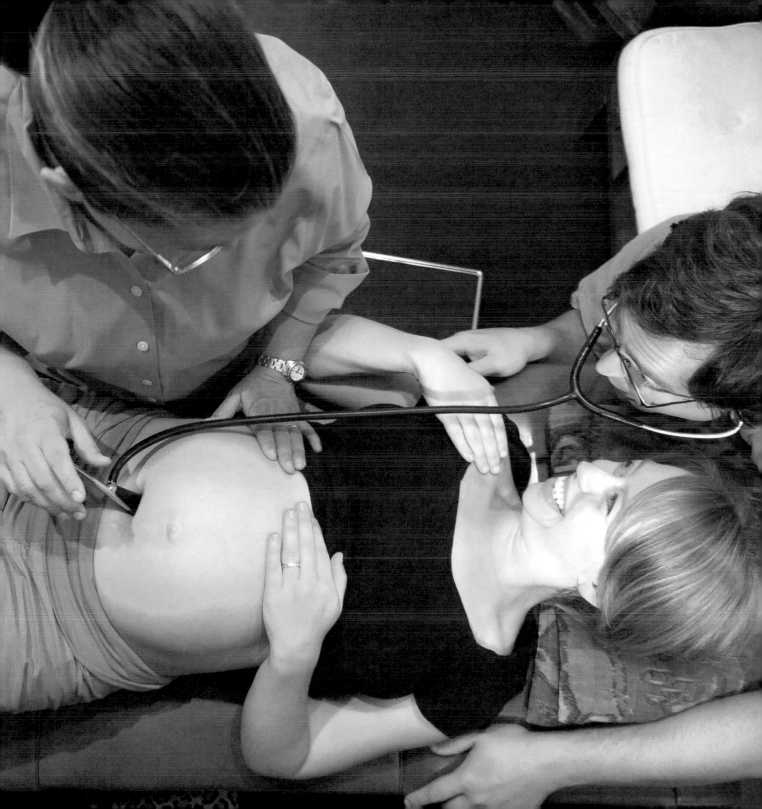

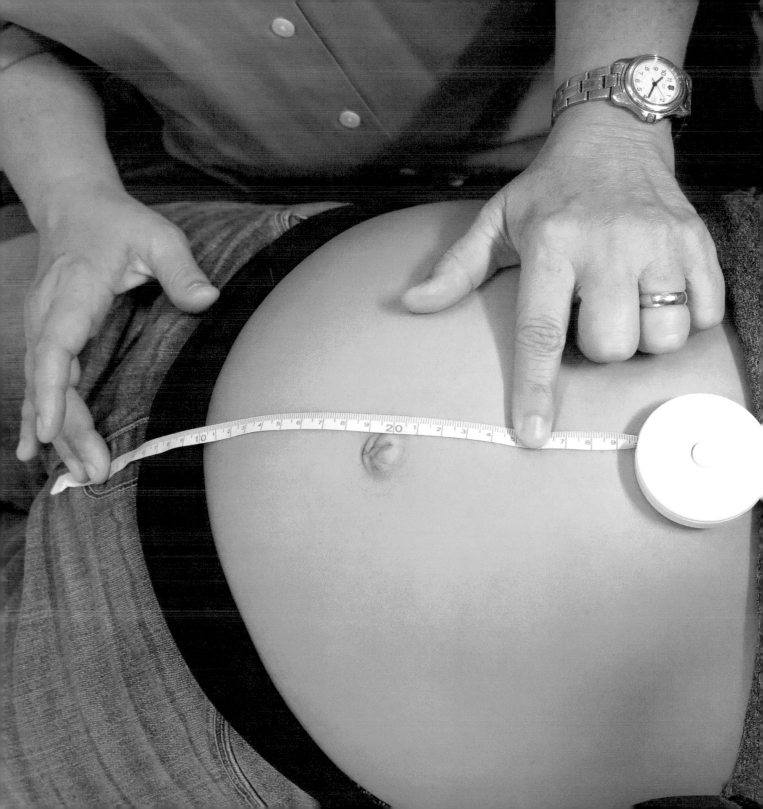

She measures the mommy's belly.

One day, my Mommy goes into labor.

Maria the Midwife comes to our house.

My baby brother is ready to come out.

We have a birth tub in the middle of our house;

it is like a big swimming pool.

Mommy works really hard while she is in labor.

Daddy helps her.

Maria the Midwife helps too.

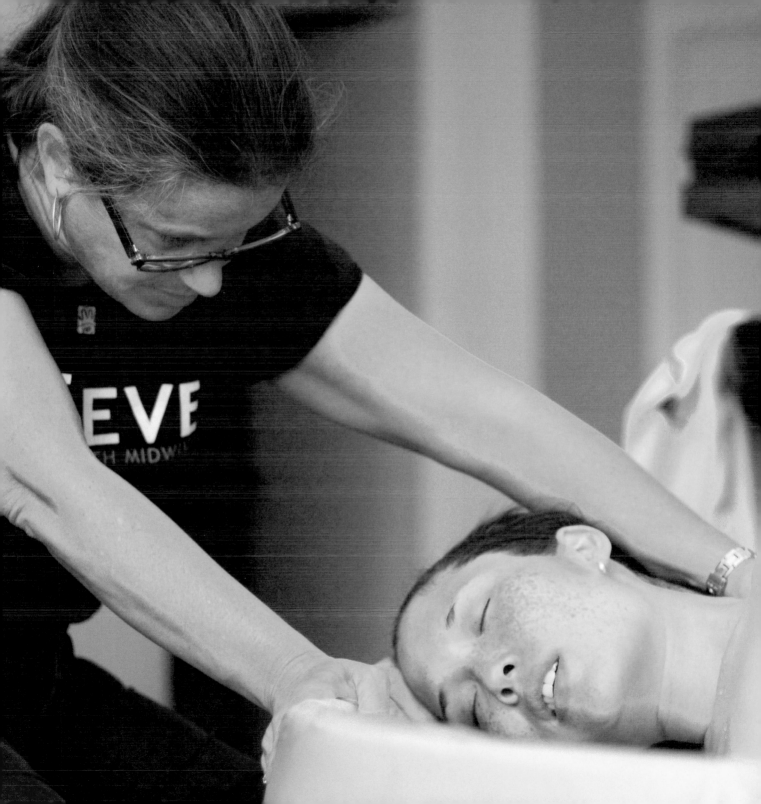

Sometimes Mommy makes funny noises.

She sits on the potty for a long time.

Maria the Midwife says Mommy is doing a good job.

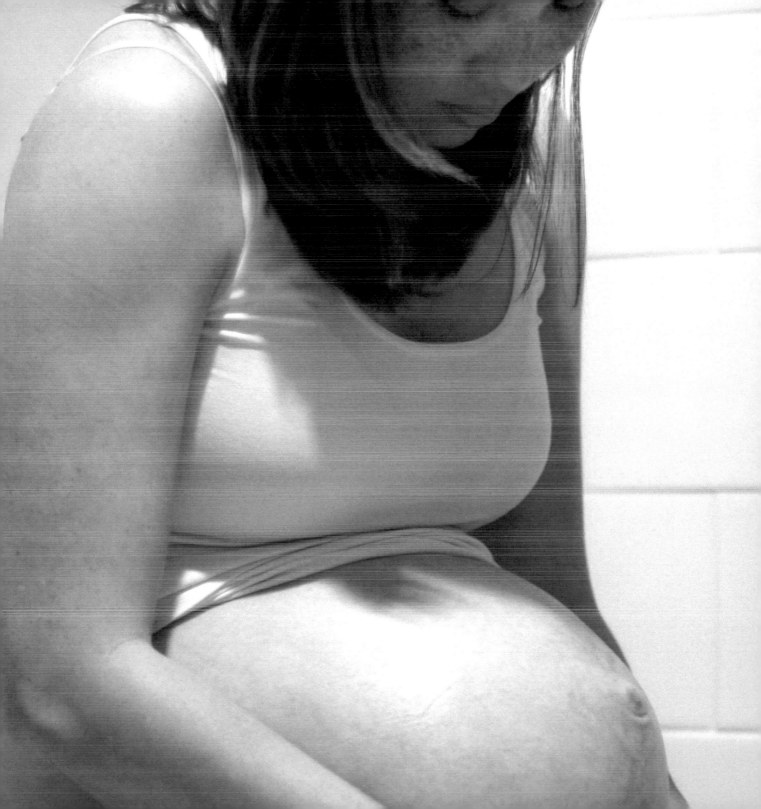

In the birth tub, Mommy pushes and pushes and pushes, and Pryce finally comes out.

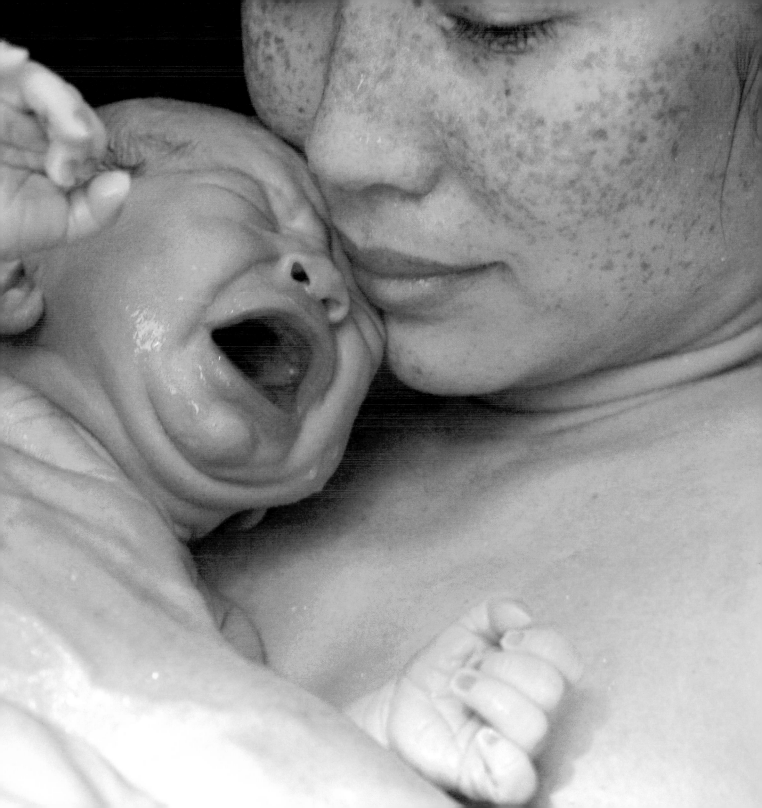

Welcome Baby Pryce!

Maria the Midwife checks my baby brother.

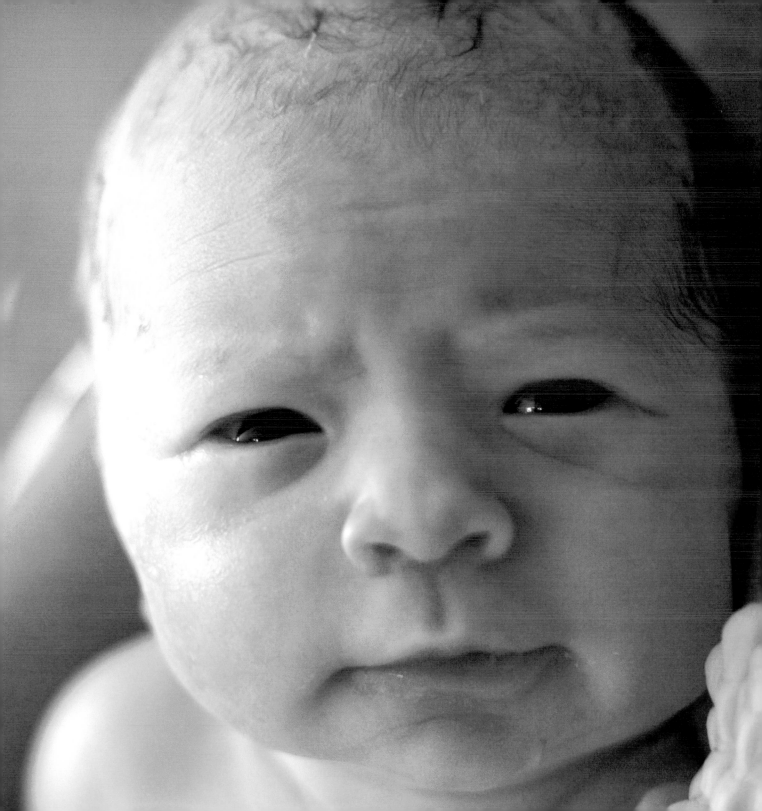

Baby Pryce is wrinkly and cute.

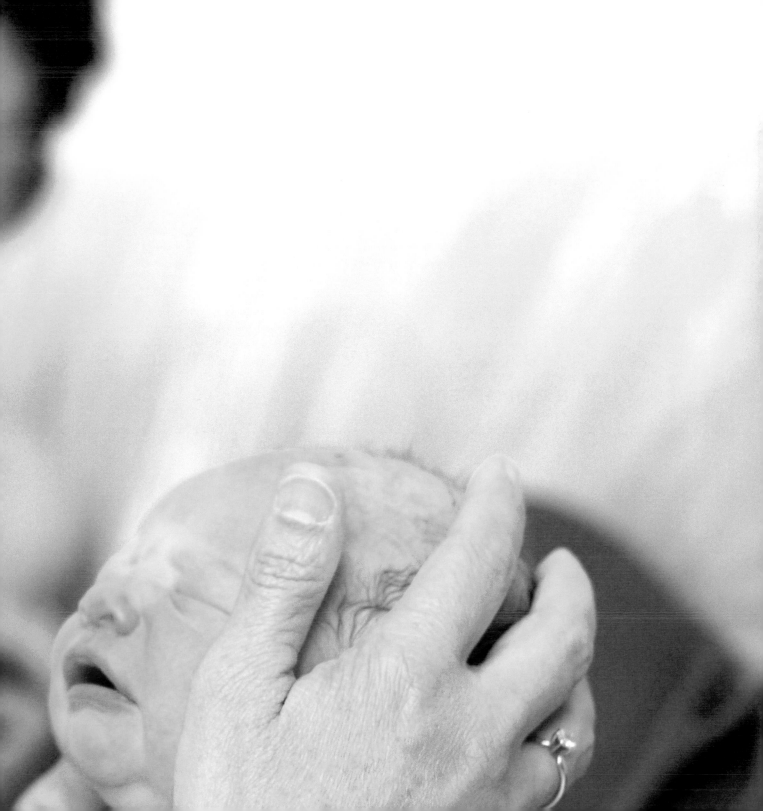

I am a BIG BROTHER!

A Xóchitl Justice Press / Wisewoman Childbirth Traditions Partnership

Xóchitl Justice Press
A nonprofit organization focusing on community partnerships, research, teaching, and publishing.

Wisewoman Childbirth Traditions
Catching babies at home and assisting hospital births in the San Francisco Bay Area since 1986.

Authors

Maria Iorillo (Maria the Midwife)
www.wisewomanchildbirth.com

Melanyann Garvin (Mommy)

Photography

Suzannah Weening

Made in the USA
Columbia, SC
13 June 2024

Born at Home

Maria Iorillo & Melanyann Garvin

Photography by Suzannah Weening

Born at Home

Xóchitl Justice Press, San Francisco, CA

Library of Congress Control Number: 2015938257

ISBN: 9781942001348

Oct 2015

10 9 8 7 6 5 4 3 2 1

To all the new siblings